How to S Groovy Chick

An essential *Bubblegum* guide

Ged Backland and Phil Renshaw

Groovy Chick

She's wild, she's hip and crazy
she makes other girls quite sick
She's fantastic and she's funky
she's a gorgeous, groovy chick!

Groovy Chick

Groovy Chick is the original IT girl. To put it quite simply she is 'The Chick'. Everything about her says 'groovy'! She's a fun-loving, stylish babe, who everyone adores. She passed all her exams at the Ministry of Cool with flying colours. Bright 'n' breezy, she leaves a trail of enthusiasm wherever she goes and always carries her trademark flower with her.

Most Likely to Say... Hello Sunshine

Most Likely to Be... Anywhere that's fun

Fave Colour Sunshine Yellow

Bestest Friends with...

Cool Dude

Hippy Chick

Happenin' Babe

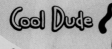

When there's a party goin' on
with tons of fun and noise
You'll always find Groovy Chick
chatting up cute boys!

When bestest mates are having fun
you'll find Groovy Chick
Having coffee with Cool Dude
cos' he's so bloomin' slick.

Groovy Chick just loves the beach
but she won't sit and fry
She'll sit in the shade, drink lemonade
and watch the world go by.

Disco Diva flaps about
dancing the macarena
Groovy Chick just sits a while
and waits for something saner!

Groovy Chick loves flowers
and so does Hippy Chick
Together they spend hours
choosing what to pick!

When the sun shines on Slaphead's bonce
it gets all freckled and flustered
Groovy Chick thinks it looks just like
a yummy big egg custard!

Groovy Gal is just so hip
a funky mover - wow!
Groovy Chick prefers a field
chatting to a cow!

At night Boy Racer likes to cruise
he loves posing in his car
But Groovy Chick would rather sit
and wish upon a star!

When Diamond Geezer comes around
offering good advice
Groovy Chick gives him a flower
'cos he's so flippin' nice!

When Old Git goes on about
how good things used to be
Groovy Chick just nods her head
and makes him a cup of tea.

Designer Diva thinks that labels
give her street cred power
But Groovy Chick knows it's best
to hold a big fat flower!

Veggie likes to see Groovy Chick
and invites her round to lunch
As animals are their bestest friends
it's lettuce leaves they munch.

When Nutty Moo acts real mad
and bungee jumps from high
Groovy Chick just stands back
to watch her bounce on by!

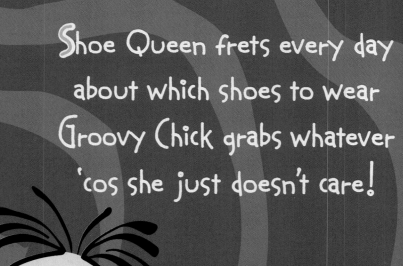

Shoe Queen frets every day
about which shoes to wear
Groovy Chick grabs whatever
'cos she just doesn't care!

So there you have it, it's all very clear
The low-down on Groovy Chick is here.

If it all sounds familiar, if it rings true
Chances are, Groovy Chick's you!